Real-Life Science
PHYSICS

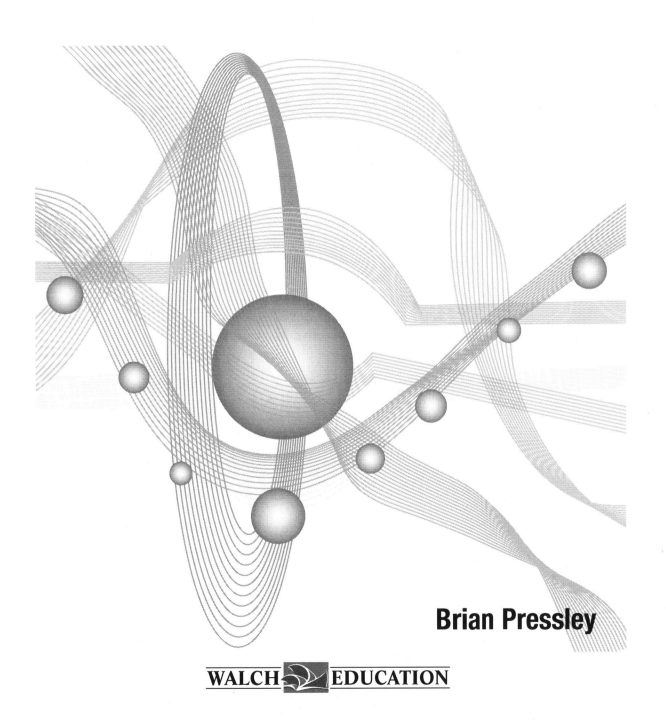

Brian Pressley

WALCH EDUCATION

1   2   3   4   5   6   7   8   9   10
ISBN 978-0-8251-6335-7
Copyright © 2008
J. Weston Walch, Publisher
40 Walch Drive • Portland, ME 04103
www.walch.com
Printed in the United States of America

Table of Contents

Introduction

The *Real-Life Science* series is designed to engage students with topics of high interest that involve places, phenomena, technology, and concepts that they may encounter in their everyday lives. The topics were chosen by professionals in science education, and the National Science Education Standards were used to develop lessons that addressed a number of content standards. Each book in the series has a correlations chart that shows core standards that are addressed by each lesson, as well as other standards that are addressed, but are not the main focus of the lesson.

Using "real-life" examples is a technique that is well supported by the National Science Teaching Standards as well. The list below includes some of the standards that suggest that quality instruction can and should include material that does more than just require students to memorize and repeat basic facts.

Teaching Standard A

Teachers of science plan an inquiry-based science program for their students.

- Select science content and adapt and design curricula to meet the interests, knowledge, understanding, abilities, and experiences of students.

Teaching Standard B

Teachers of science guide and facilitate learning.

- Focus and support inquiries while interacting with students.

- Orchestrate discourse among students about scientific ideas.

Teaching Standard E

Teachers of science develop communities of science learners that reflect the intellectual rigor of scientific inquiry and the attitudes and social values conducive to science learning.

- Structure and facilitate ongoing formal and informal discussion based on a shared understanding of rules of scientific discourse.

- Model and emphasize the skills, attitudes, and values of scientific inquiry.

Each book in the *Real-Life Science* series features lessons you can use in your classroom today. Use these engaging lessons to help your students explore the intriguing ways that science is at work all around them.

National Science Education Standards Correlations

C = Core standard   X = Other or optional skill

Title	Physical Science Content Standard B Grades 9–12: Structure of atoms	Physical Science Content Standard B Grades 9–12: Structure and properties of matter	Physical Science Content Standard B Grades 9–12: Chemical reactions	Physical Science Content Standard B Grades 9–12: Motions and forces	Physical Science Content Standard B Grades 9–12: Conservation of energy and increase in disorder	Physical Science Content Standard B Grades 9–12: Interactions of energy and matter	Science and Technology Content Standard E Grades 9–12: Understandings about science and technology	Science in Personal and Social Perspectives Content Standard F Grades 9–12: Personal and community health
1. What If You Fell Out of an Airplane Without a Parachute?				C	X			X
2. How Do the airbags in Cars Work?			X	X		X	C	
3. How Does Bulletproof Glass Work?	X	C		C	X		X	X
4. What Would Happen If You Were in an Elevator and the Cable Broke?				C			X	X
5. What Are the Long, Straight Clouds Coming from Passenger Jets?			C		X			
6. Why Isn't Normal Air Used in Race-Car Tires?		X		C			X	X
7. How Do Air Conditioners Work?					C		X	
8. What Is a Light Emitting Diode (LED), and How Does It Work?	X	X				C	X	
9. What Is a Liquid Crystal Display (LCD), and How Does It Work?		X				C	C	
10. How Are Movies Put on DVDs?		X				C	C	
11. What Is a DVR, and How Does It Work?		X				C	C	
12. How Do Digital Cameras Work?		X				C	C	
13. How Does a Rechargeable Battery Work?		X	C		X	X	X	

National Science Education Standards Correlations

C = Core standard   X = Other or optional skill

Title	Physical Science Content Standard B Grades 9–12: Structure of atoms	Physical Science Content Standard B Grades 9–12: Structure and properties of matter	Physical Science Content Standard B Grades 9–12: Chemical reactions	Physical Science Content Standard B Grades 9–12: Motions and forces	Physical Science Content Standard B Grades 9–12: Conservation of energy and increase in disorder	Physical Science Content Standard B Grades 9–12: Interactions of energy and matter	Science and Technology Content Standard E Grades 9–12: Understandings about science and technology	Science in Personal and Social Perspectives Content Standard F Grades 9–12: Personal and community health
14. How Does a Call Find My Cell Phone?						C	C	
15. How Can So Many Music CDs Fit on a Digital Music Player?		X				C	C	
16. How Do Microphones and Speakers Work Together?						C	C	
17. Why Do Some Clothes Rapidly Change Color in the Sun?	X	C			X	X	X	
18. Is the Moon Bigger When It's Near the Horizon?				X		X		
19. How Long Can a Human Survive in Outer Space?		X				X	X	C
20. How Do We Know How Much a Planet Weighs?				C			X	
21. How Do Automatic Doors Know When to Open?				X		X	C	
22. How Does a Microwave Oven Heat Food?						C	X	X
23. How Big Is a Nuclear Explosion?					X	C	X	X
24. How Does a One-Way Mirror Work?						C	X	
25. Where Does Static Electricity Come From?	C					X		

National Research Council. *National Science Education Standards*. Washington, DC: National Academy Press, 1996.

National Research Council. "National Science Education Standards." http://books.nap.edu/readingroom/books/nses/6e.html#csa912.

1. What If You Fell Out of an Airplane Without a Parachute?

Topics

gravity, terminal velocity, air resistance

Goal

To help students understand the various forces and circumstances that affect the behavior of a falling body, in particular a human body, as it falls from an airplane

Context

Students have continually increasing access to a wide variety of extreme sports, either through actual participation, print media, video, or video games. As a consequence, they are interested in unusual events in physics and some of the extreme conditions that the human body can withstand.

Teaching Notes

- Demonstrate the effect air resistance has on a falling body by comparing the fall rate of two objects, perhaps a crumpled piece of paper and a flat piece of paper of the same mass.

- Clarify the nature of terminal velocity. Students need to understand that the object is still falling; it is simply no longer accelerating.

- Ask students to share examples of falls they have taken or have heard about that were survived with little or no injury. Ask for examples they have heard of that resulted in serious injury, particularly falls that happened from low heights.

Extension Activity

Ask students to find examples of people surviving a fall out of an airplane. Have them be sure to include the circumstances that allowed the falling person to survive. Make a list with the class of the various circumstances that might protect them should they ever find themselves falling without a parachute.

Answer Key

1. a		6. d
2. d		7. b
3. b		8. a
4. c		9. d
5. c		10. d

1. What If You Fell Out of an Airplane Without a Parachute?

Explanation

Of course, little experimentation has been done on humans to determine the answer to this question. With that in mind, we are left with what we have learned from people who have fallen from planes by accident, or were left falling without the benefit of a parachute during a skydiving mishap.

The short answer is: It would be very bad. An object accelerates at around 9.8 m/s² (32 ft/s²) due to the pull of gravity near Earth's surface. Even with air resistance factored in, a person will reach terminal velocity in 10 to 20 seconds, depending on the altitude from which he or she starts falling. In this case, terminal velocity is the highest speed a person will reach before the effects of air resistance keep the person from accelerating any more. For most people, this speed is somewhere around 193 km/h (120 mph). Speed does depend on the angle of the falling body, weight, and the aerodynamics of the clothing the person is wearing.

The end result of the fall depends on the material landed on. The result can be anything from cuts, scrapes, and bruises, to severe injury or death. Falls from as low as simply standing on the ground have been fatal under the right conditions. Most falls in excess of 15 meters (about 50 feet) have a high chance of being lethal. People have survived falling from airplanes from a variety of altitudes, including as high as 6,100 meters (20,000 feet). They have survived by landing in or on things such as water, thick vegetation, trees, freshly plowed ground, sand, swamps, haystacks, power lines, car roofs, awnings, deep snow, and slanted surfaces.

Some people who have survived falls from great heights have done so in the wreckage or part of a plane that was damaged or failed in flight. Some were entangled in a partially opened parachute or clung to a second person whose parachute deployed properly. Some were even in the remains of a crashing hot-air balloon.

Name _____   Date _____

1. What If You Fell Out of an Airplane Without a Parachute?

Circle the letter of the best choice to complete each sentence.

1. The acceleration due to gravity at Earth's surface is _____.

    a. 9.8 m/s^2
    b. $9.8 \text{ m}^2/\text{s}$
    c. 32 m/s^2
    d. $32 \text{ m}^2/\text{s}$

2. It generally takes a skydiver _____ to reach terminal velocity.

    a. 5 to 8 seconds
    b. 5 to 8 minutes
    c. 10 to 20 minutes
    d. 10 to 20 seconds

3. The highest speed a falling object reaches before it stops accelerating due to air resistance is called _____.

    a. maximum velocity
    b. terminal velocity
    c. maximum speed
    d. terminal speed

4. Terminal velocity for the average person is around _____.

    a. 193 mph
    b. 120 km/h
    c. 193 km/h
    d. 120 m/s

5. The terminal velocity of a falling object is not affected by _____.

    a. the weight of the object
    b. the shape of the object
    c. the color of the object
    d. gravity

(continued)

Name _____   Date _____

assessment page

1. What If You Fell Out of an Airplane Without a Parachute?

6. A possible result of falling from a plane without a parachute is _____.

    a. scrapes
    b. broken bones
    c. death
    d. all of the above

7. The highest altitude a person has survived falling from without a parachute is _____.

    a. 9,500 meters
    b. 6,100 meters
    c. 8,900 meters
    d. 1,600 meters

8. If you fell from an airplane without a parachute, _____ would provide a relatively safe landing location.

    a. thick vegetation
    b. concrete
    c. a brick building
    d. a highway

9. Falls in excess of _____ are often lethal.

    a. 0 meters
    b. 5 meter
    c. 10 meters
    d. 15 meters

10. Things to try and land on if you fall out of an airplane include _____.

    a. car roof
    b. deep snow
    c. sand
    d. all of the above

2. How Do the Airbags in Cars Work?

Topics

acceleration, microelectromechanical systems

Goal

To help students understand the basic components of an important safety feature

Context

Competing car manufacturers continually tout the high-quality safety features in their cars. Airbags are so useful, in fact, that they are starting to appear in a wide variety of locations in the car. They are certainly not restricted to just the steering wheel anymore. This is an opportunity for students to see the various technological advances that make airbags possible.

Teaching Notes

- Ask students to share experiences they have had, seen, or heard about that involve the deployment of an airbag.

- Estimate the kinetic energy your average student would have at the time of a collision if the student was traveling at 20 meters per second (45 miles per hour). Have students use the formula for determining kinetic energy: $KE = \frac{1}{2} \cdot m \cdot v^2$
  where m = mass of object
  v = speed of object

- Clarify the word *microelectromechanical* for students. They may be confused by its length, but the roots *micro-*, *electro-*, and *mechanical* are simple enough taken one at a time. Microelectromechanical systems are small integrated devices or systems that combine electical and mechanical components.

Extension Activity

Have students find data or deployment times for various airbags. Ask them to find the speed at which the airbag deploys into the passenger compartment. Students can also research why the deployment speeds have been decreased in newer cars.

Answer Key

1. three

2. nylon or other synthetic

3. powder

4. sodium hydroxide or NaOH

5. NaN_3

6. 0.01 to 0.04

7. accelerometers

8. metal

Real-Life Science: Physics

2. How Do the Airbags in Cars Work?

Explanation

Airbags can be found in many places in a car, such as in front of the front passenger seat, in the doors, and in the frames around the doors. An airbag is made of a few simple parts, and a few components that can be very complicated in modern vehicles. There are three basic parts to most air-bag systems. There is the bag itself, which is usually made of some sort of nylon or other synthetic fabric. The bag is usually packed with a powder around it. This powder acts as a lubricant so that the bag can smoothly inflate. Most companies use talcum powder or cornstarch. After a collision, however, a small amount of caustic sodium hydroxide ($NaOH$) powder might be released during the chemical reaction that inflates the airbag.

The second basic part is the inflation mechanism. This fills the airbag during a collision. One common way airbags are inflated is by the ignition of a chemical called sodium azide (NaN_3). The sodium azide is lit with an electrical igniter. It burns like a solid propellant burns in a rocket. The nitrogen gas (N_2) created by the reaction can fill the airbag in as quickly as 0.01 to 0.04 seconds! The bag itself is not airtight like a balloon. Tiny holes in the fabric of the bag let the nitrogen gas escape so the bag can be quickly deflated.

The third part of the air-bag system is the sensors. These determine when there is a sudden change in the velocity of the vehicle and send a signal to inflate the airbag. These sensors generally contain a device called an accelerometer. An accelerometer can measure any sudden increase or decrease in speed, or even a change in direction as with a side-impact collision. The accelerometer is an example of a microelectromechanical system. This type of system contains a microscopic mechanical component—in this case, a piece of metal that slides. It also contains an electrical component. This electrical component is an integrated circuit that processes information and decides when to deploy the airbag.

2. How Do the Airbags in Cars Work?

Complete each sentence by writing the missing word or words on the line.

1. There are _____ basic parts to most air-bag systems.

2. Many airbags are made of _____.

3. Airbags usually have _____ packed around them to allow them to deploy smoothly.

4. The dust released during an air-bag inflation can include some caustic _____.

5. The chemical formula for sodium azide is _____.

6. Airbags can fill in as little as _____ seconds.

7. The small devices that detect sudden changes in the velocity of the car are called _____.

8. The mechanical component of the microelectromechanical system in an airbag is a sliding piece of _____.

3. How Does Bulletproof Glass Work?

Topics

polymers, laminates, polycarbonates

Goal

To show students how the kinetic energy from a bullet is dissipated by the laminate structure of bullet-resistant glass

Context

Students have probably seen images of bulletproof glass with damage from bullets. They can probably think of a number of places where bulletproof glass is used. This lesson shows students that the term *bulletproof* is a little misleading and clarifies how bulletproof glass succeeds or fails.

Teaching Notes

- Ask students to name places where they have seen bulletproof glass or where they know it is used.

- Discuss with students descriptive terms such as *fireproof, bulletproof,* and even *foolproof.* Have them speculate about the extent to which these words are true.

- Draw the alternating layers of glass and polycarbonate found in bulletproof glass, and illustrate the properties of each layer.

Extension Activity

If you can find a piece of bulletproof glass to show students, it is usually easy to see the alternating layers from the side, or if the glass has been broken already. If a piece cannot be obtained, have students search for images or descriptions of bulletproof glass.

Recommended web site:
http://science.howstuffworks.com/question476.htm

Answer Key

1. b	6. j
2. f	7. e
3. d	8. i
4. h	9. c
5. a	10. g

glass layer

polycarbonate layer

3. How Does Bulletproof Glass Work?

Explanation

Just as most materials aren't really fireproof, there are few things that are actually bulletproof. At best, the glass described here should be called *"bullet-resistant."* Most modern-day "bulletproof" glass has been designed to stop small weapons fire. But it would not be effective, for example, against powerful hunting rifles.

Bulletproof glass is part of a group of materials called *laminates*. In any material that is a laminate, there are individual layers that have been joined together. You may have seen such layering in a sheet of plywood. In the material we refer to as bulletproof glass, the alternating layers are usually glass and some kind of polycarbonate material. Polycarbonates are *polymers* made of long chains of carbon and oxygen atoms. Like many polymers, which are long chains of repeating units of atoms, the polycarbonates are flexible and very strong.

When a bullet hits the bulletproof glass, a number of things happen. The alternating layers have different effects on the bullet. The glass layer is very hard, but it is also very fragile. When the bullet hits the glass, the glass is able to slow the bullet somewhat, but it cannot stop the bullet by itself. After passing through the glass layer, the bullet hits the polycarbonate layer. The polycarbonate layer is strong and flexible. It absorbs a large amount of the bullet's kinetic energy. The energy from the bullet is spread through the flexible layer, and the bullet slows a great deal. By repeated collisions with alternating layers of glass and polycarbonate, the bullet eventually loses enough energy to stop.

Bulletproof glass can be as thin as a single sheet of polycarbonate plastic, about 5 to 10 millimeters (0.2 to 0.4 inches). Some military vehicles use very sturdy glass that can be up to 120 millimeters (4.7 inches) thick. Such glass can be extremely heavy. If visibility is not an important factor, there are lighter materials that are not transparent that stop bullets even more effectively.

Real-Life Science: Physics

3. How Does Bulletproof Glass Work?

Match the description on the left with the letter of the correct term on the right. Write the letter on the line.

_____   1. term that is more accurate than *bulletproof*   a. glass layer

_____   2. material made up of individual layers joined together   b. bullet-resistant

_____   3. long chains of carbon and oxygen atoms   c. kinetic energy

_____   4. made of repeating units of atoms   d. polycarbonate

_____   5. laminate layer that is hard but fragile   e. 5 to 10 millimeters

_____   6. laminate layer that is strong and flexible   f. laminate

_____   7. the thinnest bulletproof glass   g. hunting rifle

_____   8. the thickest bulletproof glass   h. polymer

_____   9. absorbed from a bullet that hits bulletproof glass   i. 120 millimeters

_____ 10. a weapon not generally stopped by bulletproof glass   j. polycarbonate layer

4. What Would Happen If You Were in an Elevator and the Cable Broke?

Topics

gravity, safety, acceleration

Goal

To clarify the various ways that people are protected from acceleration and sudden stopping in the event of an elevator failure

Context

A staple of many horror movies and even sitcoms is the failure of an elevator. Some people have an irrational fear that the elevator they are in is going to fail and they will fall to their doom. The fear of falling may not be irrational, but the fear that it will happen in an elevator is. This lesson should illustrate the various mechanisms that are in place to protect passengers from rapid acceleration and even more rapid stopping.

Teaching Notes

- Ask students if they have ever seen a news story about an elevator falling many floors and killing someone inside. They may think they have, but it's more likely they are thinking of all the fictional occurrences they have seen.

- Draw a rough image of an elevator showing all of the devices mentioned in the lesson. They need not be exactly as found in a real elevator shaft, but should serve to indicate the number of things that would have to fail for an elevator to fall.

- Explain to students that at least in the United States, elevators have to hold almost 8 times the limit they say they can hold, while a typical bridge only has to hold 2 times the posted limit.

Extension Activity

Have students find some real diagrams of working elevators. Work with students in class to identify all the safety features on the elevator, as well as some of the other methods elevators use to move besides cables.

Answer Key

1. multiple cables   6. air resistance
2. all of the load   7. shock absorbers
3. tracks and cables 8. 20.4 meters
4. governor   9. Few
5. counterweights   10. wouldn't

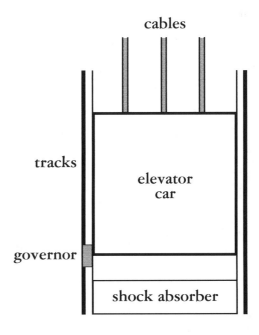

4. What Would Happen If You Were in an Elevator and the Cable Broke?

Explanation

For most modern elevators, the answer to this question would be "not much." Most elevators today have multiple cables. Any of these cables is supposed to have the carrying capacity to hold the entire elevator with its load. Therefore, elevators are very safe. Few, if any, people are killed while in elevators that fall down a shaft. Far more elevator-related injuries or deaths are connected to events in which people fell into already open shafts without an elevator, or were in the shaft doing maintenance and had an accident.

If, however, all of the cables were to break at once, there are still even more safety devices that could protect passengers. Most elevator cars are attached to and running on tracks. A device called a *governor* is activated when an elevator's speed gets too high. The governor deploys clamps that grab the tracks to slow the car, or in some cases, inserts metal rods into depressions in the tracks.

What if the governor fails to work after all of the cables have snapped? Many elevators have counterweights that prevent them from accelerating rapidly. Should even the counterweights fail, many elevator shafts are tight-fitting, and the air resistance caused by the air trying to get around the car would slow the car somewhat. Unfortunately, not all elevator shafts are designed like this. Some have systems of vents that prevent a buildup of pressure that would be high enough to slow an entire elevator.

The last line of defense is a shock absorber that most elevators land on when they reach their lowest stop. If all of the other safety devices failed, the shock absorber wouldn't stop the car smoothly, but it might provide enough reduction in speed to prevent life-threatening injuries.

People sometimes think that jumping up into the air at the last second might protect a person from injury if the elevator fell. If the car was traveling at 20 meters per second (about 45 miles per hour), you would have to jump up at 20 meters per second to be stopped relative to the ground. If you could jump at that speed outside, you would go up 20.4 meters (about 67 feet) into the air. Even if you could do it, you'd hit the roof of the elevator at that speed instead of the floor!

Name _____   Date _____

4. What Would Happen If You Were in an Elevator and the Cable Broke?

Circle the best choice in parentheses to complete each sentence.

1. Most elevators have (a single cable, multiple cables).

2. An elevator cable can carry (only part of the load, all of the load) of an elevator.

3. Most elevators are running on (tracks and cables, only cables).

4. The (governor, restrictor) is a device that deploys clamps if the elevator is moving too quickly.

5. Elevators have (counterweights, parachutes) that prevent them from accelerating rapidly.

6. Elevators may be slowed in some elevator shafts by (fans, air resistance).

7. At the bottom of most elevator shafts, there are (wooden beams, shock absorbers).

8. If you could jump at 20 meters per second, you could go (20.4 meters, 67 meters) into the air.

9. (Few, Many) people are killed while inside falling elevators.

10. Jumping at the last second before impact in a falling elevator (would, wouldn't) help.

5. What Are the Long, Straight Clouds Coming from Passenger Jets?

Topics

contrails, combustion, vapor

Goal

To clarify the composition of the condensation trails seen behind high-flying aircraft

Context

Students have probably seen the long, white clouds behind high-flying aircraft, and have probably seen several planes at once with these clouds behind them. The lesson is designed to explain how these clouds form.

Teaching Notes

- Ask students where they have seen contrails in the past. Behind high-flying planes? Low-flying planes? Fast-moving or slow-moving planes?

- Clarify that the higher a plane goes, the lower the pressure and the lower the temperature it is exposed to.

Extension Activity

Have students find out what substances, other than water, come out in the exhaust from a large passenger jet.

Answer Key

1. T

2. F; Jet fuels contain large amounts of carbon and hydrogen.

3. F; When jet fuels are burned, they give off mostly carbon dioxide and water.

4. T

5. T

6. F; At very high altitudes, contrails are mostly made up of frozen water.

7. F; As air pressure drops, the amount of water vapor air can hold decreases.

8. T

5. What Are the Long, Straight Clouds Coming from Passenger Jets?

Explanation

There are two major causes for the clouds you see forming behind an airplane as it flies far overhead. These clouds are called *contrails*. The word *contrail* is a shortened form of the phrase *condensation trail*. Contrails are clouds formed from condensed water vapor. We most commonly see these clouds formed by the passage of a passenger jet. Like most planes, the passenger jet burns fuel. As that fuel burns, it gives off a number of products. Jet fuels are composed of large amounts of carbon and hydrogen. When these substances are burned in the presence of oxygen, they give off carbon dioxide and water as the two main by-products.

At any given time, there is a limit to the amount of water vapor the air can hold, depending on temperature and pressure. When that amount is exceeded, the particles collect together and form droplets that are large enough to see. When enough of these droplets form in one place, the result is a cloud. As the air temperature gets lower, the amount of water that the air can hold decreases. Airplanes fly at altitudes where the temperature could easily be below 0°C, and as a consequence, the water is more apt to form into clouds. Generally the temperature is so low at these altitudes that if you see a contrail, it is probably made up of ice crystals because the condensed water particles have frozen.

The second factor that helps the clouds form is pressure. As the air pressure drops, the air is less able to hold water vapor, and the water vapor is more likely to condense out into visible droplets. A low-flying fighter jet, for example, may have low-pressure areas around the tips of the wings. This allows the formation of small contrails that seem to be coming off the ends of the wings. In general, air pressure is lower at highter altitudes, making the formation of contrails more common in high-flying planes.

Name _____   Date _____

5. What Are the Long, Straight Clouds Coming from Passenger Jets?

If the statement is true, write T on the line. If it is false, write F and rewrite the statement to make it true.

_____ 1. The word *contrail* is a shortened form of the phrase *condensation trail*.

_____ 2. Jet fuels contain large amounts of carbon and mercury.

_____ 3. When jet fuels are burned, they give off mostly carbon dioxide and sodium chloride.

_____ 4. When too much water vapor is in the air, it can condense out into visible droplets.

_____ 5. As air temperatures decrease, the amount of water vapor the air can hold decreases.

_____ 6. At very high altitudes, contrails are mostly made up of frozen alcohols.

_____ 7. As air pressure drops, the amount of water vapor air can hold increases.

_____ 8. Low-flying fighter jets may have areas of low pressure around their wingtips.

6. Why Isn't Normal Air Used in Race-Car Tires?

Topics

nitrogen, pressure, traction, friction

Goal

To explain the effects of putting nitrogen into tires instead of regular air

Context

Modern car racing has become very popular, and the technology involved is discussed regularly by people who follow the events. The popularity of nitrogen as a tire filler in the various racing circuits has led many businesses to offer nitrogen fill-ups for your car when you get new tires or have your car serviced. Most students know that regular air is about 78% nitrogen to start with, so does any of this matter, or are people really getting their money's worth?

Teaching Notes

- Ask students what components are in the air they breathe. Get a feel for how familiar they are with the makeup of the atmosphere. (The atmosphere is 78% nitrogen and 21% oxygen.)

- Clarify the damaging effects that oxygen can have on many materials. Students will be familiar with rusting, and some may be familiar with "dry rot" in rubber tires that are left exposed to air for a long time.

- Remind students that a surface such as that found in a rubber tire is unlikely to be completely airtight. Some small particles may pass directly through the surface, while others will leak out around valves and covers.

Extension Activity

Ask students to find out how much it costs at local garages to get four tires filled with air versus having them filled with nitrogen. Have them ask if the mechanics or attendants can give reasons why nitrogen is better than regular air.

Answer Key

1. the 1970s

2. 78% nitrogen and 21% oxygen

3. Small changes in pressure affect the traction of a race-car tire, and at speeds over 300 kilometers per hour, the changes could cause an accident.

4. For most everyday cars, nitrogen in the tires will not affect traction to any noticeable degree.

5. water and oxygen

6. one third the rate of air-filled tires

7. Constantly changing pressure can cause wear and tear on the various parts of a tire.

8. Keep the tire pressure at the recommended levels.

6. Why Isn't Normal Air Used in Race-Car Tires?

Explanation

Some race-car drivers have been filling the tires on their cars with nitrogen since the 1970s. Nitrogen is used in military vehicles and aircraft, as well. You might remember that the atmosphere is made up of about 78% nitrogen to begin with, so does topping off the other 22% really make a difference? The answer is yes and no. Race cars operate under extreme conditions that regular cars are seldom exposed to. The constant travel at very high speeds can cause temperature fluctuations that increase and decrease the pressure in the tires. A change in pressure can cause a change in the traction of a tire. At speeds in excess of 300 kilometers per hour (about 185 miles per hour), a small change in traction could be the difference between winning or losing, and even between life or death.

While filling the tires on your car with nitrogen probably won't make a big difference in terms of traction, there are some advantages. Tires filled with pure nitrogen contain almost no water vapor and almost none of the 21% oxygen usually found in the atmosphere. This helps slow down the chemical breakdown of the interior of the tire. However, unless you keep the tires for an extremely long time, this factor isn't likely to matter too much. The big advantage is that a tire filled with nitrogen loses pressure at about one third the rate of a tire filled with air. This is good for consumers because when tire pressure is too low, mileage suffers, and this can be expensive. Also, as the pressure goes up and down in the tire, the various parts of the tire suffer more wear and tear, such as the steel belts, the rubber itself, and the valves used to inflate or deflate the tire. For the average car owner, if you keep a careful eye on the pressure in your tires, regular air will be just as good as nitrogen—until you get behind the wheel of your first race car.

6. Why Isn't Normal Air Used in Race-Car Tires?

Answer the following questions.

1. How long have race-car drivers been filling their tires with nitrogen?

2. What percent of the atmosphere is made up of nitrogen? Of oxygen?

3. Why would a change in tire pressure be dangerous for a race-car driver?

4. If you're looking to change the traction of your tires, will nitrogen help?

5. What two damaging materials are found in a tire filled with air that are not found in a tire filled with nitrogen?

6. How much slower does a tire filled with nitrogen lose pressure compared to a tire filled with air?

7. Why is constant fluctuation in pressure bad for tires?

8. What simple step can you take with regard to tire pressure that can save you money?

7. How Do Air Conditioners Work?

Topics

refrigeration cycle, adiabatic expansion

Goal

To illustrate the various steps that the liquids and vapors inside an air conditioner go through to produce a stream of cool air

Context

Students know that cold air blows into a room from an air conditioner, and most have the mistaken belief that "cold" is being blown into the room. This lesson helps to illustrate that it is heat being removed from the air instead.

Teaching Notes

- Remind students that "cold" doesn't move from place to place, heat does. Remind them that a warm drink can be cooled by ice cubes, but cold doesn't flow into the drink: heat flows into the ice cubes, which is why they melt.

- Clarify the process of adiabatic expansion. In step 3 of the refrigeration process, this is what causes the sudden temperature drop in the vapor/liquid combination.

- Ask students to name other examples of things that use the refrigeration cycle.

Extension Activity

Mini refrigerators often have an easily exposed refrigeration system. If you or a student has access to one, or to a broken air conditioner, it is relatively easy to find the various parts where the five steps of the refrigeration process take place to show students. Be sure not to open any pipes or valves as some refrigerants are not safe to handle.

Answer Key

1. d	6. c
2. b	7. b
3. c	8. a
4. d	9. a
5. a	10. b

7. How Do Air Conditioners Work?

Explanation

You might be surprised to discover that your air conditioner is really just like your refrigerator without an insulated storage space around it for the food. Both appliances use the refrigeration cycle to move heat from where it isn't wanted. In the case of the refrigerator, the unwanted heat is in the food. In the case of the air conditioner, the unwanted heat is in the air of your home.

The refrigeration process commonly used in your air conditioner works with a system made up of a compressor, a condenser, an expansion valve, and an evaporator. Look at the diagram below to see where each of the five steps for a typical air-conditioning unit occurs.

1. The motor runs the compressor, which compresses a gas such as ammonia, Freon, or tetrafluoroethane. The gas experiences an increase in temperature.

2. The hot gas flows into the condenser. The condenser is a series of coils that have a fan blowing across them, which carries the heat outside. If you have ever been near the outside exhaust of an air conditioner, you know that it can be quite a bit hotter than the surrounding air.

3. The gases are cooled until they become a liquid under high pressure. Then they flow through the expansion valve. The sudden decrease in pressure causes the liquid to boil and almost immediately vaporize, although some of the liquid remains. The energy for the boiling process comes from the liquid itself, so its temperature drops significantly.

4. The vapor is now in the evaporator, where the temperature in the coils is well below the freezing point of water. A second fan blows across these coils carrying warm air from inside the room, which is then cooled and blown back out into the room.

5. The cold vapor in the coils picks up some heat from the warm air, and continues back to the compressor. There it is compressed again, and the cycle starts all over.

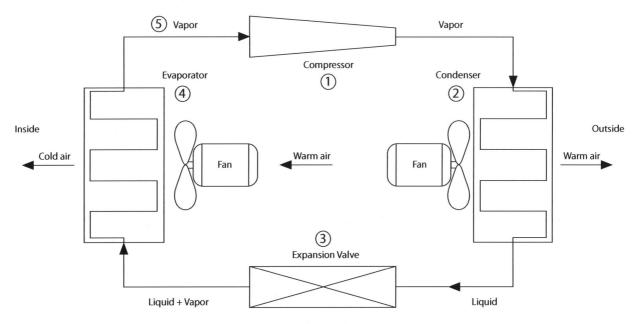

assessment page

7. How Do Air Conditioners Work?

Circle the letter of the best choice to complete each sentence.

1. An air conditioner works very similarly to _____.

    a. a television
    b. a blender
    c. an oven
    d. a refrigerator

2. The refrigeration cycle moves _____ from where it isn't wanted.

    a. cold
    b. heat
    c. air
    d. Freon

3. Air conditioners remove unwanted heat from _____.

    a. water
    b. solids
    c. air
    d. stoves

4. Air conditioners have _____.

    a. a compressor
    b. a condenser
    c. an evaporator
    d. all of the above

5. One common refrigerant is _____.

    a. tetrafluoroethane
    b. carbonite
    c. sodium chloride
    d. copper (II) sulfate pentahydrate

(continued)

7. How Do Air Conditioners Work?

6. A window air conditioner usually dumps its excess heat _____.

   a. inside of the house
   b. into a water pipe
   c. outside of the house
   d. inside of itself

7. The cool air that blows into your room from a window air conditioner _____.

   a. started out outside of the house
   b. started out inside of the house
   c. is made in the air conditioner
   d. is a refrigerant called Freon

8. The cold vapor that passed through the evaporator next goes to the _____.

   a. compressor
   b. condenser
   c. expansion valve
   d. flange sprocket

9. Between the condenser and the expansion valve the refrigerant is a _____.

   a. liquid
   b. solid
   c. vapor
   d. plasma

10. When the liquid flows through the expansion valve and boils, the energy to make it boil comes from _____.

   a. outside
   b. itself
   c. the evaporator
   d. the motor

8. What Is a Light Emitting Diode (LED), and How Does It Work?

Topics

diodes, light emission, p-type, n-type, depletion zone

Goal

To clarify the makeup and behavior of LEDs

Context

LEDs are being used to do numerous jobs that used to be done by conventional lightbulbs. As more and more LEDs appear, students may wonder why we don't simply call them lights. This is a chance to see how a new technology is taking over the job of an older technology.

Teaching Notes

- Clarify the difference between n-type and p-type materials. N-type material has an excess of negatively charged particles, while p-type material has an excess of positively charged particles.

- Ask students to identify all of the places they've seen LEDs. They may not be aware that some of the things they thought were tiny lightbulbs are actually LEDs.

- Ask students if they can think of any advantages of using LEDs instead of lightbulbs.

Extension Activity

Have students research the advantages of using LEDs instead of lightbulbs. For example, they might learn that LEDs come on faster than a regular lightbulb. This makes them ideal for brake lights, since they give a driver who sees the lights more time to respond.

Answer Key

1. Answers will vary. Sample answers: in traffic lights, in brake lights, in remote controls, as power indicators on computers.

2. light-emitting diode

3. electricity

4. n-type

5. p-type

6. depletion

7. conduction

8. photons

8. What Is a Light Emitting Diode (LED), and How Does It Work?

Explanation

Today, it is likely that you are surrounded by LEDs. They are found in traffic lights, brake lights, remote controls, as power indicators on computers and other electronic equipment, and in hundreds of other places. The acronym LED stands for *light-emitting diode.* To understand the LED, it's best to understand what a diode is and how it works. A diode is sort of like a one-way street in an electric circuit. It generally allows the flow of electricity in only one direction. Some basic diodes are made out of two connected layers. One of the layers is made up of a material referred to as *n-type* because it has extra negatively charged particles. In this case, the negatively charged particles are electrons. The other layer is made up of a material referred to as *p-type* because it has extra positively charged particles. These particles exist because of a number of "holes" where the material is missing negative charges.

When the n-type side of the diode has the negative terminal of a battery hooked to it and the p-type side has a positive terminal hooked to it, the electrons move from the n-type side to the p-type side. In effect, some of the holes move from the p-type side to the n-type side. This allows a flow of electrons to move across the diode. However, if you hook the battery up in the opposite direction, the holes are attracted to the negative terminal and the electrons to the positive terminal. This leaves an empty area in the middle of the diode, called a *depletion zone.* No charges flow across this section, which means there is no complete circuit for the electricity to follow.

So how does the LED make light? The visible light we see is the result of excited electrons in an atom falling from higher energy levels to lower energy levels and emitting the excess energy as photons of different frequencies. When electrons are moving as electricity, they are in an area called the *conduction band.* Here they have more energy than when the atom is in its ground state. This means that any time electrons fall back into the lower energy levels, such as the holes in the p-type material, photons are emitted and we see light.

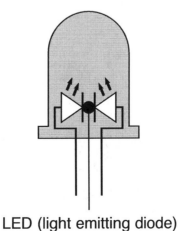

LED (light emitting diode)

25

Name _____   Date _____

8. What Is a Light Emitting Diode (LED), and How Does It Work?

Complete each sentence by writing the missing word or words on the line.

1. One place LEDs are found is _____.

2. The acronym LED stands for _____.

3. Diodes generally allow the flow of _____ in only one direction.

4. Material referred to as _____ has an excess of negatively charged particles.

5. Material referred to as _____ has an excess of positively charged particles.

6. An area that forms in the middle of the diode that will not allow electrons to flow is called the _____ zone.

7. The area where electrons are moving as electricity is called the _____ band.

8. When electrons fall back to a lower level from a higher level, _____ are emitted and we see light.

9. What Is a Liquid Crystal Display (LCD), and How Does It Work?

Topics

liquid crystals, molecular behavior

Goal

To clarify how the materials in an LCD behave to create images

Context

Technological advances mean that LCD screens are very common. From gigantic televisions to digital cameras, cell phones, and even portable DVD players, LCDs have started showing up everywhere. Faced with near-constant exposure to LCDs, students will benefit from understanding how these devices work.

Teaching Notes

- Ask students to name all of the objects they have seen that have an LCD screen. When they think about it, the list will be quite long.

- Clarify that basic LCDs, such as on a digital watch or a calculator screen, are very simple, while color LCDs, such as on a laptop, are multilayered and have sophisticated light sources and digital processors that make them work.

- Describe a polarized film and how two such films at 90° to each other can completely block light from passing through them.

Extension Activity

Using polarized film or two pairs of polarized sunglasses, have students explore how turning the lenses can increase or decrease the amount of light that passes through them. Draw a comparison to the twisting of the molecules in the liquid crystal.

Answer Key

1. i	6. g
2. j	7. c
3. a	8. f
4. h	9. b
5. d	10. e

9. What Is a Liquid Crystal Display (LCD), and How Does It Work?

Explanation

The acronym LCD stands for *liquid crystal display.* If you think back to earlier science classes, you may remember that many solids contain a series of repeating particle patterns called a *crystal lattice.* The particles are in fixed locations and are oriented mostly in a constant direction. In a liquid, however, the particles are not in fixed positions. There is little, if any, uniformity as to which way the particles point. This makes it seem like the phrase *liquid crystal* contradicts itself, but it doesn't.

The liquid crystals used in LCDs are molecules that can be changed in shape or orientation by an electric current. Without electricity running though them, the liquid crystals appear in one shape or point in one direction. When the electricity runs through them, they change shape or point in a different direction. The shape or orientation of the liquid crystals changes how light is transmitted through them. This means that in some orientations, the light can be passed through, while in others, it can be changed in color. In still others, the light can be completely blocked. This allows the LCD to keep some parts of a display clear while others are dark. Simple LCDs, like those you might find on a digital watch or an inexpensive calculator, rely on external light sources. As you might know, a calculator or a digital watch cannot be seen in the dark unless it has a built-in light source of some kind. Such simple LCDs are made of six layers. From the front, they are as follows:

1. a vertically polarized film
2. a transparent set of electrodes
3. a layer of liquid crystals
4. a second set of transparent electrodes
5. a horizontally polarized film
6. a reflective surface, such as a mirror

When electricity is applied to the electrodes in layer 4, the molecules arrange into a configuration between the electrodes that blocks the light from passing through an area in the shape of the electrodes. LCDs that are more complicated than a calculator screen, such as a laptop screen or a big-screen LCD television, have more layers to allow for the various combinations of color that are possible. They also require an internal light source.

28

Name _____ Date _____

9. What Is a Liquid Crystal Display (LCD), and How Does It Work?

Match the description on the left with the letter of the correct term on the right. Write the letter on the line.

_____ 1. the acronym for the term *liquid crystal display*

_____ 2. state of matter containing particles in fixed locations that are oriented in a mostly constant direction

_____ 3. the repeating particle patterns in a solid

_____ 4. state of matter containing particles that are not in fixed locations with little or no uniformity in the direction in which the particles point

_____ 5. molecules that can be changed in shape or orientation by electric current

_____ 6. the first and fifth layers of a simple LCD screen

_____ 7. the second and fourth layers of a simple LCD screen

_____ 8. required component of a device needed to view a simple LCD such as a watch in the dark

_____ 9. requirement for color LCD screens

_____ 10. final layer in a simple LCD

a. crystal lattice

b. more layers

c. sets of transparent electrodes

d. liquid crystals

e. mirror

f. built-in light source

g. polarized films

h. liquids

i. LCD

j. solids

10. How Are Movies Put on DVDs?

Topics

duplication, replication, digital storage

Goal

To describe the basic systems needed to store digital media, in this case movies, on DVD

Context

Constantly changing methods for storing digital media mean there are always new opportunities to learn about technology. The DVD has been around for a while, but the development of new DVD technology means that this form of digital storage is still cutting edge and will be around in some form for some time.

Teaching Notes

- Compare storage rates on CDs and DVDs for students. A byte is a group of eight binary digits processed a a unit by a computer. A typical CD can store about 740 megabytes, while a standard single-sided DVD holds about 4.7 gigabytes of data. Some double-sided DVD formats can hold about 50 gigabytes of data. Some companies are working on holographic DVDs that can hold 300 gigabytes and should eventually be able to hold about 1.6 terabytes.

- Explain that digital storage allows the computer to see or to store information as long strings of ones and zeroes.

Extension Activity

Have students compare the various storage media that they have access to. They are likely to have CDs, DVDs of varying formats, digital music players, and computer hard drives. Have them see how many CDs or standard single-sided DVDs it would take to hold all the information on their computer or digital music player.

Answer Key

1. duplication
2. A laser
3. zeroes
4. replication
5. glass
6. dust
7. stampers
8. plastics

10. How Are Movies Put on DVDs?

Explanation

Movies (or computer files) are put on DVDs in one of two ways. The first way is through a process called *duplication*. Duplication is the process of using a laser to burn the information into a surface that is designed for recording. The laser interacts with a layer of material in the recordable DVD, and does one of two things: it either changes the shape of the layer, or it changes the color of the layer. The computer in control of the recording process already has the material to be recorded in a digital format as a series of binary data made of long strings of ones and zeroes. When the laser hits the layer in the DVD, it burns millions or even billions of little pits or marks that represent the ones and zeroes. Later, when the data is retrieved, a second laser bounces off the marks and converts the different shapes back into the ones and zeroes. The computer or processor then turns the ones and zeroes back into images, sounds, or programs.

Slightly more complicated is the process of replication. For replication, expensive equipment is used, generally by a business that makes DVDs. In a special clean room, a single copy of the DVD is burned on a disc called a *glass master*. The DVD is burned by an extremely accurate laser. As with duplication, the DVD has a series of ones and zeroes burned into its surface as represented by bumps. The room is clean to avoid dust or other particles that might introduce mistakes into the surface of the glass master. Once the master is completed, it is too fragile to be used numerous times. More durable metal-coated copies called *stampers* are made from the glass master. Injection molding of polycarbonate plastics then takes place. (Polycarbonate plastics are what most CDs, DVDs, and bulletproof windows are made of.) The stampers are used to make numerous copies of the DVD. After the copies are made, one of the layers of the DVD must be coated with a reflective material. This is so the laser that will read the DVD later will be able to bounce up into the reading sensor of your DVD player.

assessment page

10. How Are Movies Put on DVDs?

Circle the best choice in parentheses to complete each sentence.

1. The process of using a laser to burn information on a DVD is called (duplication, replication).

2. (A laser, Electricity) is used to encode information onto the surface of a DVD.

3. Binary data is made up of long strings of ones and (twos, zeroes).

4. The system needing expensive equipment to make DVDs is (duplication, replication).

5. The first disc made in replication is called the (glass, aluminum) master.

6. Replication takes place in clean rooms to prevent (dust, light) from getting on the master discs.

7. Metal-coated discs called (stampers, injectors) are used to make copies in the replication process.

8. DVDs are made using polycarbonate (metals, plastics).

11. What Is a DVR, and How Does It Work?

Topics

hard drives, digital storage, digital signals

Goal

To explain how the basic components of a DVR work

Context

DVRs are rapidly replacing VCRs and DVD recorders as the most popular form of recorder for capturing video from television. The device itself is not terribly different from a computer, but recent increases in the capacity of digital storage devices have finally made them feasible to use on a larger scale.

Teaching Notes

- Ask students if they have used a VCR, a DVD recorder, or a DVR. Ask them to compare the pros and cons of each of the systems. For example, some DVDs cannot be reused, and DVRs can record in real time.

- Find out some of the maximum recording times for DVRs (this number changes almost daily) using DVD-quality video. Compare to recording on a standard single-sided DVD, which generally holds about two hours of video.

Extension Activity

Have students look up prices for a variety of DVRs. Find out which models provide the ability to record the most hours of DVD-quality video for the price.

Answer Key

1. F; DVR stands for *digital video recorder.*

2. T

3. T

4. F; The platter of a hard drive is made out of high-precision glass or aluminum.

5. T

6. T

7. F; DVRs only record digital signals.

8. F; A device called a buffer starts recording whenever you change the channel on the DVR.

11. What Is a DVR, and How Does It Work?

Explanation

A DVR is a digital video recorder. It has two components that allow it to work. The first component is the core of the DVR. This is a hard drive much like you would find inside a computer, or in a big server or mainframe. The second component is a collection of processors that allow the user to define the various tasks the DVR does, as well as to supply the user with options for using the DVR.

The hard drive is a piece of electronic equipment that is made to very demanding specifications—it has to be, or it won't work. The storage medium of the hard drive is a piece of high-precision aluminum or glass called a *platter*. The platter is mirror-smooth and contains magnetically sensitive material. The platter in some hard drives can spin up to 15,000 times per minute. This means that the outer edge can be traveling around 269 kilometers per hour (167 miles per hour). If the platter was crooked or unbalanced, the high rate of speed could cause it to destroy itself. The second major part of the hard drive is the *arm*, which is also called the *actuator arm*. The arm moves magnetic recording heads to various locations on the platter surface. Here information is recorded as magnetic flux patterns.

The processors in the DVR direct the digital signal that the DVR gets from cable or satellite to the hard drive where it is recorded. If the signal isn't digital, the processor can transform the signal into a format that can be recorded digitally. The processor also controls a buffer, which starts recording any time you change to a new channel. This means that you can "pause" a live show, or rewind a show that you have not necessarily been recording. However, most players empty this buffer when you change the channel, so you can't rewind just any show. Until DVRs have much larger hard drives, this isn't possible. The DVR would have to be recording hundreds of channels all the time, which would require an enormous amount of storage space.

Name _____ Date _____

11. What Is a DVR, and How Does It Work?

If the statement is true, write T on the line. If it is false, write F and rewrite the statement to make it true.

_____ 1. DVR stands for *durable video recorder.*

_____ 2. A DVR contains a hard drive, much like you would find in a computer.

_____ 3. Processors allow a user to define the various tasks the DVR does.

_____ 4. The platter of a hard drive is made out of high-precision plastic.

_____ 5. Some platters in hard drives spin up to 15,000 times per minute.

_____ 6. The outer edge of some hard-drive platters can be moving at over 269 kilometers per hour.

_____ 7. DVRs only record analog signals.

_____ 8. A device called a calibrator starts recording whenever you change the channel on the DVR.

12. How Do Digital Cameras Work?

Topics

pixels, semiconductors, charge-coupled devices, complementary metal-oxide semiconductors

Goal

To clarify the differences between how a traditional film camera captures an image and how the same process is accomplished with digital photography

Context

Students find themselves surrounded with devices that capture digital images. From digital cameras to cell phones, the technology is everywhere. Most students have also seen a film camera, but these cameras are rapidly disappearing. The new technology is fundamentally different, and students will benefit from understanding how it works.

Teaching Notes

- Ask students to list the pros and cons of using film or digital cameras.

- Clarify that the megapixel number provided with a digital camera seldom represents the exact number of pixels captured by the camera. Processing errors and the data-collection process itself decrease the exact number somewhat.

- Discuss the photoelectric effect and explain that the semiconductors in a digital camera use a similar effect, but the electrons generated are not ejected from the material. They are captured and sent through the processing system of the camera.

Extension Activity

Have students research the various kinds and prices of digital cameras that are available. Students should find out which cameras have the most megapixels for the cost.

Answer Key

1. Traditional film cameras rely on photosensitive film to capture images.

2. Digital cameras rely on digital storage media, such as flash memory, to store images.

3. *Pixel* is derived from the words *picture* and *element. Pix,* an abbreviation for *pictures,* is used as well.

4. A 5-megapixel camera should record about 5 million pixels.

5. Digital information is stored as a long series of ones and zeroes.

6. Digital cameras can convert light to digital information immediately.

7. CCD stands for *charge-coupled device.* It is a solar cell that sends an electric signal to the recording medium of the camera.

8. CMOS stands for *complementary metal-oxide semiconductor.* It is a solar cell that sends an electric signal to the recording medium of the camera.

12. How Do Digital Cameras Work?

Explanation

Traditional film cameras record light images on photosensitive film. The film has to be chemically developed, and then the resulting negative is used to put the image on light-sensitive paper. The paper has to be chemically treated again, and then the photographic print is completed. Instead of film and chemicals, digital cameras rely on digital recording media, such as flash memory, to record and store the images they take.

The quality of a picture that a digital camera can take is measured in pixels. The word *pixel* comes from the words *picture* and *element. Pix,* an abbreviation for *picture,* is used as well. A 5-megapixel camera is capable of taking pictures made up of about 5 million pixels. This means that you would see about 5 million little colored dots if you magnified the picture. The information for each of the pixels has to be stored digitally. Digital storage on a computer consists of recording information in the form of ones and zeroes. The information of each dot can be stored as a series of ones and zeroes by the camera, and then sent to a computer or printer. There the ones and zeroes are stored or converted back into dots of different colors.

One of the biggest differences between a film camera and a digital camera is that the digital camera is able to convert the light it receives through its lens directly into digital information. The light is focused onto a semiconductor that is one of two designs. The first of these is the charge-coupled device, or CCD. The second is the complementary metal-oxide semiconductor, or CMOS. Both kinds of semiconductors are essentially tiny arrays of many solar cells. Solar cells are able to convert light into electrons. In the semiconductors, different levels of brightness and different colors of light produce different amounts of electrons. The processing microchips in the digital camera have the ability to connect colors and brightness with the amount of electrons. The information is stored digitally, and then can be reproduced later on a video screen or as a photo print.

Name _____ Date _____

12. How Do Digital Cameras Work?

Answer the following questions.

1. What kind of recording medium do traditional film cameras use?

2. What kind of recording medium do digital cameras use?

3. How was the word *pixel* derived?

4. How many pixels can a 5-megapixel camera record at its highest quality setting?

5. How is information stored in the digital camera?

6. What is transformed immediately to digital information in a digital camera?

7. What is a CCD? What does it do?

8. What is a CMOS? What does it do?

38

13. How Does a Rechargeable Battery Work?

Topics

batteries, reversible reactions, energy

Goal

To explain a simple example of how batteries can be recharged

Context

Students have a large variety of electronic devices (laptops, digital music players, portable DVD players, and so forth) that have rechargeable batteries. Although this lesson doesn't address every kind of battery ever made, it gives a simple model that can be used to describe how many kinds of batteries are recharged.

Teaching Notes

- Explain that there are a wide variety of batteries, and that not all kinds are rechargeable.

- Clarify that not all batteries contain acids like car batteries do. Most students will think that all batteries contain acids, while in truth, many contain strong bases. Modern batteries such as lithium-ion batteries can have solid or liquid electrolyte phases that don't readily conform to simple definitions of acid or base.

Extension Activity

Have students research some of the dangers of recharging various kinds of batteries. Have them find out what kinds of recalls have happened with batteries and what prompted the recalls. Be sure that students understand what can happen if you try to recharge a battery that is not rechargeable.

Answer Key

1. d
2. a
3. b
4. d
5. a
6. c
7. b
8. c
9. b
10. d

13. How Does a Rechargeable Battery Work?

Explanation

There are a wide variety of batteries, so let's narrow the discussion down to a simple wet-cell battery such as a car battery. In some types of chemical reactions, chemical A mixes with chemical B to form chemicals C and D. Written as a chemical reaction, you might think of it as the following:

A + B $\longrightarrow$ C + D

Some reactions move in only one direction under "normal" conditions. But some reactions can be forced to go "backwards" from the most common way they behave. This type of reaction is written with a two-headed arrow to show it is a reversible reaction. Such a reaction is written as follows:

A + B $\longleftrightarrow$ C + D

In some types of reactions, however, one of the products is electrons. This type of reaction will not run backwards under "normal" conditions. This is the case in the following reaction:

A + B $\longrightarrow$ C + electrons

In a regular battery, a chemical reaction takes place in which two chemicals react and form other chemicals and an excess of electrons. These electrons collect at the negative terminal of the battery. When a circuit is completed, the electrons are free to flow in the form of electricity. Eventually chemicals A and B are used up, and the battery weakens or dies.

A rechargeable battery is recharged using an outside electrical source. What is happening, in terms of the reactions mentioned above, is that the reaction is reversible and can be forced into moving backwards:

A + B $\longleftrightarrow$ C + electrons

Look at the reaction written a different way:

electrons (energy in from an electric outlet) + C $\longrightarrow$ A + B

You can see that the addition of energy in the form of electricity has forced the reaction to run backwards, causing chemicals A and B to reform. This process isn't perfect, however. Side reactions may cause chemicals (E, F, G, H, and so forth) to form that are not chemicals that were in the battery originally. Eventually, even adding electricity back to the battery won't reform enough of chemicals A and B for the battery to work.

13. How Does a Rechargeable Battery Work?

Circle the letter of the best choice to complete each sentence.

1. The reaction A + B ➞ C + D _____.

    a. represents chemicals C and D reacting to form chemicals A and B
    b. represents chemicals A and D reacting to form chemicals C and B
    c. is reversible
    d. represents chemicals A and B reacting to form chemicals C and D

2. The reaction A + B ⬌ C + D _____.

    a. is reversible
    b. represents chemicals A and D reacting to form chemicals C and B
    c. is not reversible
    d. represents chemicals A and C reacting to form chemicals B and D

3. The reaction A + B ➞ C + electrons _____.

    a. is reversible
    b. represents excess electrons being produced
    c. represents chemical C reacting with electrons to form chemicals A and B
    d. cannot happen

4. When a battery is not part of a circuit, electrons _____.

    a. collect at the positive terminal of the battery
    b. collect outside of the battery
    c. will not collect at either terminal of the battery
    d. collect at the negative terminal of the battery

5. When chemicals A and B are used up, _____.

    a. a battery weakens or dies
    b. a battery gets stronger
    c. a battery is at half capacity
    d. a battery has only one hour of power left

(continued)

assessment page

13. How Does a Rechargeable Battery Work?

6. The reaction electrons + C ⟶ A + B represents _____.

    a. a battery being run down
    b. a reversible reaction
    c. a battery being recharged
    d. the formation of chemical C

7. Side reactions _____.

    a. double the strength of a battery
    b. form chemicals that are not desired
    c. recharge a battery
    d. create an excess of electrons in a battery

8. When chemicals A and B can no longer be reformed, _____.

    a. a battery is at half capacity
    b. a battery gets stronger
    c. a battery cannot be recharged
    d. a battery is fully recharged

9. Rechargeable batteries are recharged using _____.

    a. chemicals A and B
    b. an outside energy source
    c. in internal energy source
    d. chemicals A and C

10. A reaction that can happen in both directions is called _____.

    a. rechargeable
    b. irrechargeable
    c. irreversible
    d. reversible

14. How Does a Call Find My Cell Phone?

Topics

mobile phones, switching, radio frequency

Goal

To clarify the process by which a single mobile phone is located

Context

Many students have cell phones. As the number of phones increases, the system needed to manage all of the calls and other capabilities is becoming more and more complex. This lesson is designed to help illustrate how any complex system can be broken down into a number of simpler components.

Teaching Notes

- Ask students to name all of the various kinds of cell phones they have seen or used. Take a quick poll to see how many students have a cell phone. Ask them to estimate how many cell phones are in service in the United States. There are currently hundreds of millions.

- Ask students what other types of information they can send or receive over their phones.

Extension Activity

Have students find out the frequencies that are used by cell phones in the United States. The U.S. government has an allocation chart that students can find on the Internet that shows the various frequencies and what devices they are assigned to.

Recommended web site:
www.ntia.doc.gov/osmhome/allochrt.html

Answer Key

1. mobile identification number and/or system identification code

2. five-digit

3. system identification code

4. roaming

5. cell-phone tower

6. two frequencies

7. to your phone

8. strength

9. two-way radio

10. cell

14. How Does a Call Find My Cell Phone?

Explanation

You probably know that there are some numerical codes that are part of your cell phone that help the cell-phone network find it. One is the mobile identification number. This is connected to the phone number another person might dial to reach your phone. Another number is the system identification code. This is a five-digit number that the Federal Communication Commission (FCC) has assigned to your cell-phone service carrier.

When you turn on your phone, it searches for the system identification code. This tells the phone if it's in your carrier's network, if it's out of range completely, or if you are on another carrier's network (referred to as *roaming*). Once a connection is made to the network, the local mobile telephone switching office acknowledges that your phone is in service and determines which cell your phone is in. The word *cell* in the phrase *cell phone* doesn't actually refer to the phone—it refers to an area around a cell-phone tower. And just as a number of cells make up your body, the telephone cells make up the body of the cell-phone network.

When a call enters the system looking for your phone, the various databases at the mobile telephone switching offices are searched for your mobile identification number. The mobile telephone switching office has an automated system run by computer programs. When the correct cell is found, this automated system assigns two frequencies to your cell phone for the duration of the call. Your phone basically becomes a two-way radio. One frequency carries information leaving your phone. One frequency carries information coming into your phone. This allows you to talk while the person on the other end is talking, and you can both be heard.

If you are moving, the switching office computers keep track of the strength of the signal. As the signal weakens in one cell and strengthens in another, it will eventually be handed off to the cell where the signal is the strongest.

Name _____   Date _____

14. How Does a Call Find My Cell Phone?

Complete each sentence by writing the missing word or words on the line.

1. Your phone is identified by the _____.

2. The Federal Communication Commission (FCC) has assigned a _____
    number to your cell-phone service carrier.

3. When your phone first turns on, it looks for the _____.

4. When you are on another carrier's network, it is referred to as _____.

5. The word *cell* refers to the area around a _____.

6. Computers at the mobile switching office assign _____ to your phone
    for each call.

7. Your phone has a frequency that carries information away from your phone and one
    that carries information _____.

8. The mobile switching office tracks the signal _____ of your phone
    when you are moving.

9. Your mobile phone is essentially a _____.

10. When your signal strength is too low, the signal is handed off to another
    _____.

15. How Can So Many Music CDs Fit on a Digital Music Player?

Topics

digital storage, computer file format, file compression

Goal

To compare the different methods of storing digital music files

Context

In recent history, music recording formats have evolved from records and 8-tracks to iPods® and computer hard drives. Students know that digital music players will store an enormous amount of music, but they are less aware of the fact that currently they trade away about 90% of the original recording to allow for so much storage.

Teaching Notes

- Ask students if they know the storage amount on a typical CD. Remind them of the comparative values of megabytes versus gigabytes. (A megabyte contains over one million bytes, while a gigabyte contains over one billion bytes.)

- Discuss with students the various ways they store music, and ask them to share the various amounts of storage space they have at their disposal.

- Ask students if they know of the various file extensions that are found on music files, and see if they have any idea why different types of files exist. Clarify that different types of compressed music files are made with different programs that make unique assumptions about what parts of the music most people hear and enjoy.

Extension Activity

Have students provide data with respect to the various devices they use to store music. Students can describe memory, number of songs in storage, and total number of songs that can be stored. Have them estimate how long they could listen to a full music player before running out of new songs.

Answer Key

1. d	6. f
2. g	7. e
3. b	8. i
4. j	9. h
5. a	10. c

15. How Can So Many Music CDs Fit on a Digital Music Player?

Explanation

There are a variety of formats for storing music files. Common file types are MP3 (Moving Pictures Expert Group Audio Layer III or MPEG-3), WAV (Waveform), AIFF (Audio Interchange File Format), Au (Audio), AAC (Advanced Audio Coding), MP4 (MPEG-4 Part 14 files, also called m4a), and WMA (Windows Media Audio).

All these file types, and many others, are designed to represent music or other audio in a digital format. This means that, for example, music can be converted to a series of ones and zeroes that are stored on internal flash memory, or in some cases, on a miniature hard drive.

The original music file that you find on a CD generally takes up 40 to 50 megabytes of space. This means that a standard CD can hold between 15 and 18 average-length songs. The compression process is one of the factors that allows digital music players to hold so many songs. It can compress the files until they only take up 4 to 5 megabytes. Various computer programs have been written that take a standard sound file that is 40 to 50 megabytes and carefully remove sound information found in the file that is not easily picked up by the human ear. However, many professional musicians and people who study sound professionally can hear these sounds. This leads to complaints about the quality of some of the compressed versions of the songs. The greater the compression, the less of the original sound recording that is left to be played back.

The storage media inside a digital music player is the main reason why so many songs can be stored. A single standard CD has about 740 megabytes of storage space. It is common for a digital music player to have 40 gigabytes of storage, or even more. A digital music player of this size could hold 800 to 1,000 normal CD audio files, which means it could hold 8,000 to 10,000 compressed files.

assessment page

15. How Can So Many Music CDs Fit on a Digital Music Player?

Match the description on the left with the letter of the correct term on the right. Write the letter on the line.

_____ 1. the abbreviation for Moving Pictures Expert Group Audio Layer III music file

a. AIFF

_____ 2. the number of megabytes for an average original music file on a CD

b. WAV

_____ 3. the abbreviation for the Waveform music file format

c. AAC

_____ 4. the average number of songs that fit on a CD in original format

d. MP3

_____ 5. the abbreviation for the Audio Interchange File Format music file format

e. WMA

_____ 6. the average size in megabytes of a compressed music file format

f. 4 to 5

_____ 7. the abbreviation for the Windows Media Audio music file format

g. 40 to 50

_____ 8. the average storage size in megabytes for a CD

h. 8,000 to 10,000

_____ 9. the approximate number of compressed files a 40-gigabyte storage device could hold

i. 740

_____ 10. the abbreviation for Advanced Audio Coding

j. 15 to 18

16. How Do Microphones and Speakers Work Together?

Topics

microphones, speakers, induction, vibration

Goal

To clarify the simple connection between a speaker and a microphone

Context

Speakers and microphones have almost identical components and are found in an increasing number of devices. These items take advantage of some basic concepts such as vibration and induction, and use them to perform a wide variety of tasks.

Teaching Notes

- Explain the process of induction to students and illustrate, if possible, using an ammeter connected to a coil and magnet pair.

- Ask students to explain how they think of the hearing process. Do they know about the vibrations?

- Draw simple diagrams of a microphone and a speaker, and point out the similarities in the components—the coils, magnets, and so forth.

Extension Activity

If the equipment is available, have students record sounds using a microphone, and then have them try to record the same sounds by using a speaker as a microphone. Be sure that the connectors for the speaker will fit into the jack for the microphone before trying this with a class.

Answer Key

1. vibrations
2. electricity
3. diaphragm
4. stationary
5. varying
6. an amplifier
7. diaphragm
8. sound waves
9. thin diaphragm
10. microphone

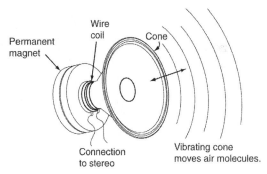

Loudspeaker

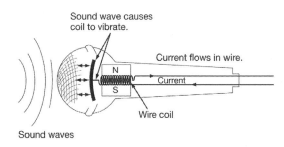

Microphone

49

Name _____   Date _____

16. How Do Microphones and Speakers Work Together?

Explanation

There are a few basic facts that you need to know before you can understand how a microphone or speaker works. The first is that sound is made up of vibrations that pass through the air around us. These vibrations are picked up by your eardrums and are then converted to electrical signals that are interpreted as sound by your brain. A second fact is that when you move a piece of wire through a magnetic field in a certain manner, you can generate electricity in the wire. While these two facts may seem unrelated, they are the basics of how a microphone and speaker work.

There are many types of microphones. A very basic design can be made with a thin diaphragm, a magnet, and some wire. The diaphragm acts like the eardrum in your ear. Vibrations that are passing through the air, such as from the voice of a speaker, enter the microphone and cause the diaphragm to vibrate. The diaphragm is connected to wires. As those wires vibrate, they pass through a stationary magnetic field. Different frequencies and intensities cause the diaphragm to vibrate in different ways. This causes the wires to move back and forth in the magnetic field, which generates a varying current in the wires. This current is usually carried to an amplifier, which then sends it to a speaker or to a recording device that can record the variations in the electric current generated by the microphone.

On the opposite end of this setup is the speaker. The speaker is nearly the exact same thing as a microphone, but is usually larger and designed to focus or direct sound away from itself. The speaker also has a diaphragm, a magnet, and wires. The microphone process is reversed, and the varying electric current from the microphone travels into the wires, which pass through the stationary magnetic field. This causes the wires that are connected to the diaphragm to vibrate, which causes the diaphragm itself to vibrate and to give off sound waves. Even without an amplifier, you can actually speak into a speaker and the sound will come out of the microphone. However, the sound produced will be very quiet.

Name _____   Date _____

16. How Do Microphones and Speakers Work Together?

Circle the best choice in parentheses to complete each sentence.

1. Sound is made up of (vibrations, electromagnetic waves) that pass through the air.

2. When you move a wire through a magnetic field, you can generate (electricity, sound).

3. The (magnet, diaphragm) in a microphone acts like the eardrum in your ear.

4. The diaphragm in a microphone is connected to wires that move through a (moving, stationary) magnetic field.

5. When the wires in a microphone vibrate through the stationary magnetic field, they generate a (varying, constant) current.

6. The current from a microphone usually goes directly to (the speaker, an amplifier).

7. Varying current passed into a speaker causes the wires hooked to the (diaphragm, magnet) to vibrate.

8. The vibrating diaphragm in a speaker gives off (radiation, sound waves).

9. One component of a microphone is a (thin, thick) diaphragm.

10. If you speak into a speaker, sound will come out of the (microphone, amplifier).

17. Why Do Some Clothes Rapidly Change Color in the Sun?

Topics

photochromism, ultraviolet light

Goal

To describe the process by which photochromic materials change color when exposed to sunlight

Context

Many students have seen eyeglasses that change color when exposed to sunlight. Now that this technology is being used in a variety of other items, students are more likely to be familiar with it.

Teaching Notes

- Ask students to share any experiences they have had with photochromic materials.

- Clarify that it is ultraviolet radiation that causes the change in the materials, which is why the materials don't change color under normal indoor lighting.

Extension Activity

Ask students if they have any photochromic materials that the class could observe. If possible, expose the items to regular light, sunlight, and a UV lamp, and make a note of how they behave in different kinds of lighting.

Answer Key

1. F; Sunglasses that change color in sunlight have been available since the 1960s.

2. T

3. T

4. F; Photochromic materials change color when exposed to ultraviolet light.

5. T

6. T

7. F; "Twisted" photochromic molecules are more likely to react with air and other chemicals.

8. F; "Twisted" photochromic molecules "untwist" when taken out of ultraviolet light.

Name _____   Date _____

17. Why Do Some Clothes Rapidly Change Color in the Sun?

Explanation

You or a friend may have a shirt that changes color in sunlight. As far back as the 1960s, there have been sunglasses that change color when exposed to sunlight. Recently, that same technology has become advanced enough to be applied to clothing, nail polish, and even toys. The materials that allow this to happen are now available in screen-printing inks. Screen printing is one of the processes by which colored images are put on T-shirts and novelty clothing items. These inks and the other items described all have the property of photochromism. This means that when these materials are exposed to ultraviolet light, they change color.

The chemicals that are found in the various photochromic items are transparent in visible light. However, when these chemicals are exposed to ultraviolet light, the molecules that are photochromic react in an unusual manner—they change shape. Normally the molecules do not absorb photons of visible light. When they are exposed to ultraviolet radiation, however, they "twist" because of changes in how the various bonds are formed between atoms in the molecules. Then they absorb different photons of visible light, which causes them to appear with a new color.

One of the drawbacks of the various photochromic materials is that when they are "twisted" by the ultraviolet radiation, they are in an arrangement that is more unstable than when they are not "twisted." Thus, they are more likely to react with the air and other chemicals they come into contact with. The more times they are exposed to ultraviolet light, or the longer they are exposed to ultraviolet light, the more worn out and less efficient they become.

When photochromic materials are taken away from the ultraviolet light source, such as inside, out of the sunlight, the molecules go back to their more stable arrangement. The colors that appeared in the sunlight slowly fade away until they can no longer be seen.

Name _____ Date _____

17. Why Do Some Clothes Rapidly Change Color in the Sun?

If the statement is true, write T on the line. If it is false, write F, and rewrite the statement to make it true.

_____ 1. Sunglasses that change color in sunlight have been available since the 1940s.

_____ 2. Some nail polish changes color in sunlight.

_____ 3. Colored images can be put on T-shirts by screen printing.

_____ 4. Photochromic materials change color when exposed to visible light.

_____ 5. The chemicals in photochromic materials are transparent in visible light.

_____ 6. Photochromic molecules change shape when exposed to ultraviolet light.

_____ 7. "Twisted" photochromic molecules are less likely to react with air and other chemicals.

_____ 8. "Twisted" photochromic molecules "untwist" when put in ultraviolet light.

18. Is the Moon Bigger When It's Near the Horizon?

Topics

moon illusion, forced perspective, zenith

Goal

To clarify the fact that the moon does not appreciably change size as it moves along its path across the sky

Context

Many students have seen the moon come up on a cool autumn evening and have marveled at how it fills the sky. Later the same night, they may have also noticed that the moon is somewhat smaller and less impressive than earlier in the evening. This lesson is designed to help them understand that it's their perception of the moon that's changing.

Teaching Notes

- Explain that the moon doesn't change size as it crosses the sky. In actuality, the moon is a little more than 1% *smaller* near the horizon because it is actually farther away when seen through the atmosphere at an angle across the horizon.

- Ask students to discuss their impressions of the phenomenon. Have they noticed it?

- Draw a picture of the moon at the horizon and at its zenith relative to Earth's surface and atmosphere. Show

students that the moon is actually a little farther away at the horizon. The picture below shows the observer at X.

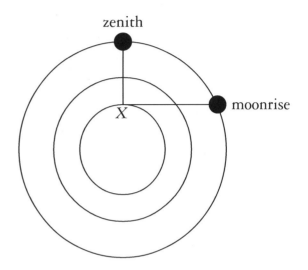

Extension Activity

Have students choose a method for measuring the relative size of the moon, and share it with classmates to see if the idea makes sense or not. If possible, have students use their testing method to see if they can measure any size difference as the moon crosses the sky.

Answer Key

1. no

2. 50% to 60%

3. In forced perspective, some form of optical illusion occurs that makes objects look bigger or smaller, or closer or farther than they really are.

(continued)

18. Is the Moon Bigger When It's Near the Horizon?

4. no

5. Refraction would make the moon look smaller.

6. A simple relative measure of the moon could be made by comparing the size of the moon to an object held at arm's length.

7. Despite years of research, there is little agreement as to why some people think the moon looks larger at the horizon.

8. The only "safe answer" is that some form of optical illusion is tricking our brains so we think the moon is larger than it really is.

18. Is the Moon Bigger When It's Near the Horizon?

Explanation

This question has been asked for thousands of years. The answer that people of every generation have eventually come to is *no.* However, there is no question that people think the moon is bigger when it's near the horizon. Numerous studies have been done in which people were asked to describe the size of the moon in various locations throughout its path across the sky. Whether people described the moon's size in terms of centimeters, inches, radians, or degrees, the studies almost always found the same thing—people think the moon looks 50% to 60% bigger near the horizon than it does at the top (zenith) of its path. The basic concept is that of forced perspective. In forced perspective, some form of optical illusion occurs that makes objects look bigger or smaller, or closer or farther than they really are.

Strangely, despite access to vast amounts of technology and many studies about the behavior of the human brain, physicists, philosophers, and psychologists cannot agree on a reason why people think the moon is larger at the horizon than at its zenith. One thing they do agree on, however, is that it is not refraction caused by Earth's atmosphere making the moon look bigger. There are two reasons why they think this. The first is that refraction would actually make the moon look smaller, not larger. The second is that if you hold up an object and take a relative measure, you will see almost immediately that the moon doesn't change size. If a ruler held up at arm's length says the moon is 3 centimeters wide at the horizon, it will say that the moon is 3 centimeters wide at its zenith.

There are many competing theories as to why the moon looks larger at the horizon. However, there is little agreement on which one is right. What is probably safe to say is that our brains are wired to interpret the location of objects in the three-dimensional world around us. This means that you probably have reflexes built into your sight that categorize things as big or small, near or far, bright or dark. Some combination of those things could be tricking your brain into thinking the moon is larger than it really is.

57   *Real-Life Science: Physics*

18. Is the Moon Bigger When It's Near the Horizon?

Answer the following questions.

1. Is the moon actually larger near the horizon?

2. How much larger do people perceive the moon to be when it's near the horizon?

3. What is forced perspective?

4. Do scientists think refraction makes the moon look bigger?

5. What effect does refraction have on the size of the moon?

6. How can a relative measure of the moon be made?

7. Is there agreement as to why the moon looks larger at the horizon?

8. What is probably the "safe answer" as to why the moon looks bigger near the horizon?

19. How Long Can a Human Survive in Outer Space?

Topics

vacuum, pressure, near-Earth conditions

Goal

To describe the conditions of outer space and their possible effects on the human body

Context

Students have seen a number of wildly inaccurate portrayals of what would happen to a person exposed to a vacuum. Explosion of the body is a popular interpretation, but it is, in all probability, completely wrong. This lesson is designed to clarify the real effects a person could expect to experience in space near Earth.

Teaching Notes

- Explain to students that most of the examples they have seen of people being exposed to space in movies and on television are exaggerated to make them more dramatic.

- Remind students that actual exposure to raw space has almost never happened to humans.

- Ask students to list all the potential factors that might affect their bodies in space, and to what extremes those factors might harm them.

Extension Activity

Have students research examples of people exposed to a vacuum and the effects that the exposure had on them.

Answer Key

1. b	6. d
2. c	7. b
3. a	8. c
4. a	9. c
5. d	10. a

19. How Long Can a Human Survive in Outer Space?

Explanation

If a person is in a well-supplied spaceship, there is no reason why he or she couldn't survive for a long time. If the person is outside of a spaceship without a space suit, he or she probably wouldn't live very long. There has been a lot of research done into the conditions of the area outside of Earth's atmosphere, as well as into the conditions of a vacuum. Fortunately, very few people have been exposed to space and then studied. As a result, there are still questions as to what exactly would happen. That being said, we do know a lot about what would *probably* happen.

The conditions in space are quite extreme. Space is a vacuum, which means there is no atmosphere and no oxygen. Assuming a person was exposed to a vacuum without warning, the average person only has about 15 to 20 seconds of oxygenated blood left to travel to the brain. When the blood starts to arrive from the lungs and it hasn't been oxygenated, the person will lose consciousness. Being unconscious would leave a person unable to deal with other components of the extreme environment. The temperature in direct sunlight in space around Earth is hotter than boiling water. The sunlight has extremely high levels of ultraviolet radiation and charged particles. In the shade, it can be more than a 100°C (180°F) below the freezing point of water, although there are no air particles to carry the heat away from the body.

You may have watched a scene in a movie in which a person exposed to a vacuum exploded because of the pressure inside of his or her body. This is unlikely to happen. It's probable, however, that the eardrums would break outward because of the internal pressure. Many of the fluids in the body would boil if exposed to a direct vacuum. As they are contained by skin, they are more likely to push against the skin and cause it to swell. After a few minutes without air, whether a person is in space or not, suffocation would occur. Space is a harsh environment, so it's probably best to remember your space suit.

60

Name _____ Date _____

19. How Long Can a Human Survive in Outer Space?

Circle the letter of the best choice to complete each sentence.

1. In the vacuum of space, there is no _____.

    a. sunlight
    b. oxygen
    c. radiation
    d. temperature

2. A person exposed to a vacuum without warning has about _____.

    a. 20 to 30 seconds of oxygenated blood
    b. 45 to 50 seconds of oxygenated blood
    c. 15 to 20 seconds of oxygenated blood
    d. 1 to 2 seconds of oxygenated blood

3. The temperature in direct sunlight in space around Earth is _____.

    a. hotter than boiling water
    b. the freezing point of water
    c. below the freezing point of water
    d. unable to be measured

4. Sunlight is full of _____.

    a. ultraviolet radiation
    b. sound waves
    c. electricity
    d. hot air

5. The temperature in the shade in space is _____.

    a. hotter than boiling water
    b. the freezing point of water
    c. more than 200°C below the freezing point of water
    d. more than 100°C below the freezing point of water

(continued)

19. How Long Can a Human Survive in Outer Space?

6. In a vacuum, you would not explode, but your _____ might.

   a. eyeballs
   b. fingers
   c. lips
   d. eardrums

7. The fluids in the body would _____ if exposed directly to the temperature in space.

   a. freeze
   b. boil
   c. sublimate
   d. melt

8. After being exposed to a vacuum in space for a few minutes, a person would _____.

   a. be fine
   b. feel stronger
   c. suffocate
   d. be safe for 5 more minutes

9. Sunlight has extremely high levels of _____.

   a. air particles
   b. cold rays
   c. ultraviolet radiation
   d. gamma rays

10. People in movies often _____ because of internal pressure when exposed to a vacuum.

    a. explode
    b. freeze
    c. burn
    d. implode

20. How Do We Know How Much a Planet Weighs?

Topics

universal gravitation, planetary mass, gravity, force

Goal

To clarify the process used to determine the weight of Earth

Context

Students see a number of constants, and many of them are complicated and hard to understand. The mass of Earth is a simple number to comprehend, but the method used to derive it is the complicated part.

Teaching Notes

- Explain to students that the process used to determine the mass of Earth was developed over a relatively long period of time and wasn't accomplished by a single individual.

- Ask students to speculate about how the mass of Earth could be determined.

- Explain to students that Newton devised the law of universal gravitation, but later scientists determined the value of G through experimentation. Henry Cavendish is considered to be the person who provided the data for the first accurate estimate of G, but he did not make a calculation of the number himself.

Extension Activity

Have students research the masses of the planets in the solar system. Have them determine how the masses were measured if we haven't been to all of the planets to repeat the experiments that allowed us to calculate the mass of Earth.

Answer Key

1. the masses of two objects separated by a distance

2. the distance between the centers of mass for two objects

3. G

4. The approximate value of G is currently 6.67×10^{-11} N · m^2/kg^2.

5. $F = \dfrac{Gm_1m_2}{d^2}$

6. $F = ma$

7. 5.97×10^{24} kilograms

8. It is the mass, because mass doesn't vary with location, while weight does.

63

20. How Do We Know How Much a Planet Weighs?

Explanation

As you advance through physics, you may eventually find yourself calculating the effects of gravity on Earth and other planets. Some of the formulas used to do these calculations require you to know the mass of a planet such as Earth or Mars, or the mass of the Moon or even the Sun. The question is how did these numbers come to exist? It's not as if you can bring Mars to Earth and put it on a big set of bathroom scales.

The problem was addressed by Sir Isaac Newton when he formulated his law of universal gravitation. The formula below gives the force of attraction F between two bodies that have masses m_1 and m_2 that have a distance of d between their two centers of mass. The letter G in the formula is the universal gravitational constant. It has been validated by experimentation many times over the years. The currently accepted value is approximately 6.67×10^{-11} N $\cdot$ m²/kg². The formula is as follows:

$$F = \frac{Gm_1m_2}{d^2}$$

We know from one of Newton's other formulas, $F = ma$, that the force exerted on a 1-kilogram mass here on Earth would be approximately 9.8 N. This means we can solve the first formula using F as 9.8 N, m_1 as 1 kilogram, and m_2 as the mass of Earth. The distance between the objects would be the average radius of Earth (about 6.373×10^6 meters). Rearranged for m_2, the formula is as follows:

$$m_2 = \frac{Fd^2}{Gm_1} = \frac{(9.8\text{N})(6.373 \times 10^6\,\text{m})^2}{(6.67 \times 10^{-11}\text{N} \cdot \text{m}^2 \,/\, \text{kg}^2)(1\text{kg})} = 5.97 \times 10^{24}\,\text{kg}$$

Notice that this is the *mass* of Earth, not the weight. Earth wouldn't really have a weight as such unless it was resting on the surface of some other planet. Remember, the *mass* of an object doesn't vary with location, but the *weight* of an object does.

20. How Do We Know How Much a Planet Weighs?

Answer the following questions.

1. What do the variables m_1 and m_2 represent in Newton's law of universal gravitation?

2. What is the distance represented by d in Newton's law of universal gravitation?

3. What variable is used to represent universal gravitational constant?

4. What is the currently accepted value for the universal gravitational constant?

5. Write the law of universal gravitation.

6. What formula was used to calculate that a 1-kilogram mass would have a force of 9.8 N exerted on it at Earth's surface?

7. What is the currently accepted value for the mass of Earth?

8. Why isn't the answer to number 7 the weight of Earth?

21. How Do Automatic Doors Know When to Open?

Topics

ultrasonics, radio, radar, automation

Goal

To explain the forces and mechanisms involved in the operation of an automatic door

Context

Students have all experienced automated doors. This lesson serves as an opportunity for them to learn about the unseen mechanisms that allow an automated door to do its job.

Teaching Notes

- Ask students to list the various locations where they have seen automatic doors.

- Ask students to list the various types of doors they have seen operate by automated systems (swinging, sliding, retracting, lifting, revolving, and so forth).

- Invite students to speculate on the types of mechanisms that might move the doors.

Extension Activity

Have students use a lightbulb and a mirror to explore the approach of an object to a broadcasting source. As the mirror gets closer to the bulb, more of the light from the bulb is returned to the general area of the bulb, just as more of the radar signal is returned to the area of the radar source as a body approaches the automated door.

Answer Key

1. T

2. F; Some automated doors have mats that have pressure sensors under them.

3. T

4. T

5. T

6. F; Some automated doors have a broadcasting device and a sensor in a small, black half-sphere over the door.

7. F; When a sensor finds an increase in the amount of broadcast signal that returns, it sends a signal that causes the door to open.

8. F; When a sensor finds a decrease in the amount of broadcast signal that returns, it sends a signal that causes the door to close.

21. How Do Automatic Doors Know When to Open?

Explanation

When you walk into supermarkets, retail stores, or other public buildings, you may notice a variety of automatic doors that open when you approach. Some swing away from you, and some slide out of your way, but somehow these doors know you're there and know to make the way clear for you. The question is: How do they know you're there?

With some of the doors, there is a mat on the ground or floor that you have to step on to activate the door. These mats are waterproof, which helps protect the wiring and pressure sensors that are under them. When you step on the pressure sensor, a signal is sent to a motor that swings or slides the door. These types of doors usually have mats on both sides. The door knows not to close until you are clear of both mats.

With other doors, the sensors might not be so obvious. You probably know that you have to be within a certain distance of the door to get it to open, but you may not have noticed the sensor that's detecting you. In some of these doors, there is a sensor that is broadcasting and then receiving one of three things: ultrasonic sound (too high to be heard by people), radio waves, or radar waves. The sensor is usually directly over the door and may appear as a small, black half-sphere. Modern sensors are also hidden in the ceiling over the doors or may be so small that they are hard to spot. All three sensors do basically the same thing. They broadcast a signal into the area around both sides of the door and then keep track of the amount of signal that returns. When the amount increases suddenly, perhaps because you've walked into the signal and more of it is bouncing back to the sensor, an electrical signal is generated inside the sensor. This signal tells the motor that controls the door to open the door. When the level of signal gets low enough again, after you've gotten through the door and out of the way of its closing, a second electrical signal is sent telling the door to close.

Name _____ Date _____

21. How Do Automatic Doors Know When to Open?

If the statement is true, write T on the line. If it is false, write F and rewrite the statement to make it true.

_____ 1. Radar, radio, and ultrasonic waves will bounce off your body to some degree.

_____ 2. Some automated doors have mats that have heat sensors under them.

_____ 3. Some automated doors have mats both inside and outside of the door.

_____ 4. Some automated doors have sensors that use ultrasonic sound.

_____ 5. Some automated doors have sensors that use radar waves.

_____ 6. Some automated doors have a broadcasting device and a sensor in a small, black half-sphere under the floor.

_____ 7. When a sensor finds a decrease in the amount of broadcast signal that returns, it sends a signal that causes the door to open.

_____ 8. When a sensor finds an increase in the amount of broadcast signal that returns, it sends a signal that causes the door to close.

22. How Does a Microwave Oven Heat Food?

Topics

microwaves, magnetrons, frequency, thermal transfer

Goal

To give a short explanation of the various components that allow a microwave to heat food

Context

The microwave oven has many mysteries associated with it, as well as a great deal of misinformation. This lesson is designed to clarify the operating principles of the microwave oven and describe some of the designs that make the microwave oven safe.

Teaching Notes

- Ask students to share any information they have about the safety features of microwave ovens. What concerns do they have, and what have they been told about how microwaves will affect them?

- Explain that microwaves escaping from an oven would be felt almost immediately.

- Remind students that although microwave ovens are very safe, there is no reason to purposefully try to expose themselves to microwaves.

Extension Activity

Have students research to find out what kind of injuries a person might sustain from direct exposure to microwaves. Have them try to find out if there have been recalls of microwave ovens that leaked microwaves.

Answer Key

1. magnetron
2. spiral
3. microwave
4. gigahertz
5. 2.45
6. do not get hotter
7. water
8. millionths
9. polar
10. cathode

22. How Does a Microwave Oven Heat Food?

Explanation

In every microwave oven, there is a device called a *magnetron*. A magnetron is a special kind of vacuum tube that can generate microwaves. Inside the magnetron, electrons are drawn from a high-temperature cathode in the center of a chamber by the positive outside walls of the chamber. However, there is a strong magnetic field in the magnetron. Instead of flying directly to the walls, the electrons travel in a spiral path around the inside of the chamber. They move past a series of cavities along the outer walls of the chamber and create high-frequency radio waves in the cavities. Some of these high-frequency radio waves are in the microwave spectrum. They are drawn off and sent into the cooking chamber.

In a typical microwave oven, the frequency of the emitted microwaves is 2.45 gigahertz. This is 2.45 billion cycles per second. Water molecules are polar in nature. This means that while the overall water molecule is electrically neutral, there are concentrations of positive and negative charge on the ends of the water molecules. The microwaves, being electromagnetic in nature, twist the water molecules back and forth 2.45 billion times per second. Free-floating water molecules in the air in the microwave oven mostly just twist back and forth. They absorb microwave radiation, but then reemit it without getting any hotter. However, water molecules in the food being cooked absorb the microwaves and are agitated. But the water molecules do not reemit the microwaves. The absorbed energy causes the water molecules to rub back and forth against one another, creating friction. In this way, the microwave energy that is created by the magnetron is passed into the water molecules in the form of heat from friction. The heat cooks or reheats the food. Some other molecules, such as fats and sugars, are also heated by microwaves.

One last thing—microwave ovens are very safe. People mistakenly believe that a microwave gives off a large amount of radiation, even with the door closed. The truth is, if the energy generated by the microwave was escaping, you would feel it as heat right away. The microwaves generated inside the oven disappear within millionths of a second when the oven goes off. No matter how hard you tried, you couldn't open the door fast enough to let the microwaves out under ordinary conditions.

Name _____ Date _____

22. How Does a Microwave Oven Heat Food?

Circle the best answer in parentheses to complete each sentence.

1. A (magnetron, voltronator) is a special kind of vacuum tube that makes microwaves.

2. The electrons inside of the magnetron travel in a (spiral, straight) path.

3. Some of the radio waves generated by the magnetron are in the (X-ray, microwave) spectrum.

4. The frequency of microwaves in a regular microwave oven is 2.45 (megahertz, gigahertz).

5. Water molecules twist back and forth in a microwave (2.45, 3.45) billion times per second.

6. When free-floating water molecules in a microwave oven absorb microwaves, they (get hotter, do not get hotter).

7. In a microwave oven, (water, salt) molecules in food rub back and forth against one another, causing food to heat.

8. When the power is shut off in a microwave oven, the generated microwaves disappear in (trillionths, millionths) of a second.

9. Water molecules are (polar, nonpolar).

10. Inside the magnetron, there is a high-temperature (anode, cathode).

23. How Big Is a Nuclear Explosion?

Topics

yield, kiloton/megaton equivalent, nuclear reactions, energy

Goal

To clarify the various terms and descriptions used to indicate the size of a nuclear explosion

Context

Nuclear bombs have the capacity to do a great amount of damage, and despite their destructive abilities, they are in some ways pinnacles of achievement in the field of physics. This lesson is to help give students some idea of the amount of energy involved in the detonation of such a bomb.

Teaching Notes

- Ask students if they are familiar with terms such as *kilotons* and *megatons*. Find out if they have any idea of the size of a nuclear explosion.

- Clarify that the lesson is not about a failure at a nuclear power plant, but is instead specifically addressing the abilities of nuclear weapons.

- Identify locations about 30 kilometers and 60 kilometers from your school to use to illustrate the size of the mushroom cloud from the 50-megaton bomb detonated in the former Soviet Union.

Extension Activity

Have students find images of nuclear explosions and see if they can locate any with scales indicating the size of the mushroom clouds or the blast zones.

Answer Key

1. c	6. d
2. i	7. f
3. a	8. b
4. g	9. e
5. h	10. j

23. How Big Is a Nuclear Explosion?

Explanation

There are a number of ways to measure a nuclear explosion. Probably the most common way is to determine the yield of the nuclear bomb. The yield is the amount of energy released by the explosion. The first nuclear weapons were compared to explosives that already existed, and the most common powerful explosive was TNT. TNT is trinitrotoluene, the main component of dynamite. The comparison is made by determining the amount of TNT it would take to make the same size explosion as the one made by the nuclear weapon. Since the explosions are so large, the terms *kiloton* (1000 tons) and *megaton* (1,000,000 tons) are used. A kiloton of TNT would release about 4.18×10^{12} joules of energy. A megaton would release about 4.18×10^{15} joules of energy.

The first test of a nuclear bomb in the United States was on July 16, 1945 in New Mexico. The bomb was called *Trinity.* The estimates of the energy that would be released when it exploded were quite varied. Some people thought it might not work at all. Others thought it might destroy half the state. The person with the best guess was Isidor Rabi, a consultant who worked at the Massachusetts Institute of Technology. He estimated the yield would be 18 kilotons, the equivalent to an explosion of 18,000 tons of TNT.

The actual yield was probably around 19 kilotons. However, the size of the explosion, the effect of the radiation on equipment, and the slightly unpredictable nature of the explosion prevented scientists from finding a highly accurate system for calculating yield.

Much larger bombs have since been made, some as large as 50 megatons. This is the equivalent of 50,000,000 tons of TNT. Such a bomb is capable of making a mushroom cloud at least 60 kilometers (about 37 miles) high and over 30 kilometers (about 18 miles) wide. The testing of one such bomb by the former Soviet Union supposedly caused minor damage as far as 1,000 kilometers (about 621 miles) from the site of the test.

Name _____ Date _____

23. How Big Is a Nuclear Explosion?

Match the description on the left with the letter of the correct term on the right. Write the letter on the line.

_____ 1. trinitrotoluene

_____ 2. the number of tons in a kiloton of TNT

_____ 3. the number of tons in a megaton of TNT

_____ 4. the number of joules of energy released by a kiloton explosion

_____ 5. the number of joules of energy released by a megaton explosion

_____ 6. the yield, in kilotons, of the first nuclear bomb tested in the United States

_____ 7. the yield, in megatons, of the nuclear bomb set off in the former Soviet Union that caused damage up to 1,000 kilometers away

_____ 8. the height, in kilometers, of the mushroom cloud known to be about 30 kilometers wide made by the nuclear bomb set off in the former Soviet Union

_____ 9. the first nuclear bomb tested in the United States

_____ 10. the person with the best guess for the yield of the first nuclear bomb tested in the United States

a. 1,000,000

b. 60

c. TNT

d. 19

e. *Trinity*

f. 50

g. 4.18×10^{12}

h. 4.18×10^{15}

i. 1,000

j. Rabi

24. How Does a One-Way Mirror Work?

Topics

mirrors, front-silvering, back-silvering, reflection

Goal

To clarify the difference between a conventional mirror and a one-way mirror

Context

One-way mirrors figure prominently in a number of movies and television shows about crime. Sometimes they are portrayed accurately, and sometimes they are not. This lesson is designed to explain how one-way mirrors work and what their limitations are.

Teaching Notes

- Ask students to talk about the various places where they have seen one-way mirrors and what they were being used for.

- Clarify that one-way mirrors will not work between two equally well-lit rooms.

- Draw a diagram showing light reflecting from a regular mirror and then compare it to a drawing of light being partially transmitted through a one-way mirror.

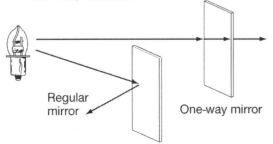

Regular mirror

One-way mirror

Extension Activity

If possible, obtain a one-way mirror and show students that it will not work with equal lighting on both sides. If you cannot get a one-way mirror, some regular CDs will act like a one-way mirror, provided there aren't too many images or a label on the top surface.

Answer Key

1. Early mirrors were made from flat metal that had been highly polished.

2. Aluminum is applied to the side of a front-silvered mirror that would be closer to the viewer (the front).

3. The sealant for a front-silvered mirror is transparent. It has to be to allow light to still reach the actual mirror surface.

4. Front-silvered mirrors are generally used in devices in which the reflection from the piece of glass that is in the front of a back-silvered mirror would be unwanted, such as in a telescope.

5. Aluminum is applied to the side of a back-silvered mirror that would be farther from the viewer (the back).

6. A one-way mirror is only half-silvered.

7. The silvering on a one-way mirror is only a few molecules thick.

8. The room on the side that is acting as a mirror must be brighter than the room on the side that is acting as a window (brighter where the "watched" are, and dimmer where the "watchers" are).

24. How Does a One-Way Mirror Work?

Explanation

The first question to answer is: How does any mirror work? There are a number of ways to make a mirror. Early mirrors were simply made of flat metal surfaces that had been highly polished. Modern mirrors are generally made in one of two ways. They are silvered, which means coated with a thin layer of metal. There are front-silvered mirrors and back-silvered mirrors. A front-silvered mirror consists of a piece of material that has a thin film of metal, often aluminum or silver, on the front of the mirror. The metal is usually sealed with a very thin coating of transparent material to keep the metal from corroding. This kind of mirror is used in devices such as telescopes to cut down on unwanted reflection from the glass that is at the front of a back-silvered mirror.

A back-silvered mirror also has a thin coating of aluminum or silver, but the coating is usually painted over with some kind of very dark sealant or paint. You can see the difference between a front-silvered mirror and a back-silvered mirror by simply putting your finger up against the surface. In a front-silvered mirror, your finger will appear to touch the reflection. In a back-silvered mirror, you will see that there is a thin space between the finger and the reflection that is the thickness of the glass.

A one-way mirror is half-silvered. Instead of the glass surface being coated completely with aluminum or silver so that no light gets through, the one-way mirror is coated with a film of metal that is only a few molecules thick. This allows for some of the light to pass through and for some of the light to be reflected. As you may have seen on television, one-way mirrors are often used for security reasons, such as in a bank or an interrogation room. The side where the person is being interviewed is kept bright so that a lot of light reflects back into the room. This gives the one-way mirror the appearance of being a regular mirror on the bright side. The other side, perhaps where the police are watching, is kept dark so that very little light is available to go through the half-silvered surface. This effect can be seen on a house with screens over the windows. When sunlight shines directly on the screens, it is very hard to see into the house. However, the people inside can still see out easily. And just as you can see in through the screen at night when it's dark outside and light inside, a person could see into the observation room if the observation room was bright and the interrogation room was dark.

24. How Does a One-Way Mirror Work?

Answer the following questions.

1. What were early mirrors made from?

2. Where is aluminum applied to a front-silvered mirror?

3. What kind of material is used to seal a front-silvered mirror? Why is this material used?

4. Where are front-silvered mirrors used?

5. Where is aluminum applied to a back-silvered mirror?

6. How is a one-way mirror silvered?

7. How thick is the silvering coating on a one-way mirror?

8. How must the brightness in the two rooms on either side of the one-way mirror compare for the mirror to work properly?

25. Where Does Static Electricity Come From?

Topics

static electricity, triboelectric series, net charge

Goal

To define and clarify the behavior of static electricity

Context

Students are somewhat mislead by the word *static* in the term *static electricity*. Although the buildup of charge may occur in a single location, even at that location the charges must move to gather together.

Teaching Notes

- Ask students to talk about circumstances in which they have received a static shock. What were the materials involved?

- Explain that lightning is an example of a large buildup of excess charge being transferred from one place to another.

- Find a triboelectric series chart online or from a text and show students where various materials are in the series.
  Recommended web sites:
  http://science.howstuffworks.com/vdg1.htm
  www.siliconfareast.com/tribo_series.htm

Extension Activity

Have students explore some basic electrostatic demos, such as rubbing a balloon on a student's hair and sticking it to the wall, or rubbing a rubber rod in a piece of silk or on a plastic bag. This can produce enough charge buildup to divert the path of a thin stream of water from a faucet.

Answer Key

1.	d	6.	a
2.	a	7.	c
3.	b	8.	b
4.	c	9.	b
5.	d	10.	d

25. Where Does Static Electricity Come From?

Explanation

You have probably experienced reaching for a doorknob after walking across a carpet and getting a nasty shock. Or perhaps you have pulled some clothes out of the dryer and heard them crackle as you tried to overpower the static cling to get them apart. The reason these events happen is because of the makeup of the materials around you. The everyday matter you see is made up of atoms. You may recall that atoms are made of protons, neutrons, and electrons. The neutrons do not carry a net electric charge and don't figure heavily in the production of static. The proton, however, has a positive charge and the electron has a negative charge.

The electrons are in a "shell" that surrounds the nucleus where the protons and neutrons are found. Some materials hold on to these electrons more strongly than others. A series, called the *triboelectric series*, compares the ability of materials to gain or lose electrons. The more positive a material is on the series, the more likely it is to give up electrons. The more negative the material, the more likely it is to capture electrons.

For example, your hair is very positive compared to the rubber material that makes up a balloon. This means that when you rub a balloon against your hair, the balloon is more likely to gain electrons. Your hair is more likely to lose electrons. Contrary to what you might think, the rubbing itself does not actually make the static. The rubbing just allows more of the surface of your hair to come into contact with the surface of the balloon. This in turn allows more electrons to transfer to the balloon. When enough electrons have gathered in one place, it is possible for them to overcome the insulating properties of the air around them and jump to another object. This creates the little bluish spark that is sometimes visible.

Incidentally, the word *static* is, in part, a carryover from a time when scientists separated electricity into various categories based on how it behaved in certain circumstances. Static electricity didn't move according to their system, but we know that when a shock travels from your finger to a doorknob or the other way around, it is doing anything but sitting still.

assessment page

25. Where Does Static Electricity Come From?

Circle the letter of the best choice to complete each sentence.

1. Electrons _____.

   a. have a positive charge
   b. have no charge
   c. are found in the nucleus of an atom
   d. have a negative charge

2. Protons _____.

   a. have a positive charge
   b. have a negative charge
   c. have no charge
   d. are found in the proton cloud

3. Electrons are _____.

   a. found in a "shell" inside the nucleus
   b. found in a "shell" outside the nucleus
   c. found in the nucleus with the neutrons
   d. never connected to atoms

4. The triboelectric series _____.

   a. orders materials by their densities
   b. orders materials by their numbers of protons
   c. orders materials by their relative abilities to capture or give up electrons
   d. orders materials by their numbers of neutrons

5. The more positive a material on the triboelectric series, _____.

   a. the more likely it is to gain electrons
   b. the more likely it is to gain protons
   c. the more likely it is to give up protons
   d. the more likely it is to give up electrons

(continued)

80

assessment page

25. Where Does Static Electricity Come From?

6. The more negative a material is on the triboelectric series, _____.

   a. the more likely it is to capture electrons
   b. the less likely it is to capture electrons
   c. the more likely it is to capture protons
   d. the heavier it is

7. On the triboelectric series, _____.

   a. neither hair nor rubber is more positive
   b. hair is less positive than rubber
   c. hair is more positive than rubber
   d. hair and rubber cannot be compared

8. When enough electrons gather in one place, _____.

   a. they repel nearby protons
   b. they can overcome the insulating properties of the air around them
   c. they attract other nearby electrons
   d. they cause electrons on the surface of a material to turn into protons

9. Static isn't caused by _____.

   a. triboelectric differences
   b. friction
   c. electrons
   d. a balloon touching your hair

10. Rubbing a balloon on your hair increases static electricity because _____.

    a. protons leap to the balloon
    b. protons leap to your hair
    c. less of the two surfaces touch each other
    d. more of the two surfaces touch each other